My h[...]

This book belongs to

_____

Written by Stephen Barnett
Illustrated by Rosie Brooks

Contents

My home 3

New words 31

What did you learn? 32

About this book

Young children are keen to explore and to enquire about their own world and the new things they come across. This story encourages children to identify with their own lives and family.

My home

This is me.

This is my home.

My father

My mother

My sister

My brother

My family

My sister is tall.

My brother is short.

I love my parents.

There are three kids.

This is our street.

Here is our home.

All of us together.

New words

all

tall

brother

family

father

home

me

mother

of

our

parents

sister

short

street

this

together

us

31

What did you learn?

What is the colour of the door of the house?

How many kids are there in the family?

How many cars are there in the street?